The World of Rod McKuen

Books by Rod McKuen

The World of Rod McKuen

Words and Music by Rod McKuen

Photographs by Helen Miljakovich

Piano Arrangements by Ben Kendall

Random House

New York

For Joe Smith

A NOTE

I write to find out about myself; what makes me turn. I never wanted to be a writer—or planned to be one. I have always been a singer who needed songs that reflected how he felt about himself and his surroundings in order to make his performance of them believable. In desperation I had to write my own material. There just weren't enough songs reflecting *me,* written by other people.

This book contains twenty-two songs—all of them personal, some of them I think are pretty good. Ben Kendall's arrangements have captured the songs as I wanted them to be. The photographs were taken by Helen Miljakovich. She has invaded, perhaps, a bit more of my world than I'd planned. But she's done so with kindness, intelligence and talent.

People ask me what I like to do best—write poetry, songs, sing, whatever. I don't play favorites. My work, if I can call it that, is all I am. What I write and perform is an extension of myself. *The World of Rod McKuen* is limited to what I know and what I continue to find out about myself and the people and places and thoughts that take me out of myself and into the larger world. I'm not very far into that world yet, but I'm a little further along than I was yesterday.

These songs and this book are a gift to those who've been able to make me have a world at all.

Rod McKuen
London, June 1968

Contents

The World
of Rod McKuen

I'm Strong But I Like Roses

People Change

blows;   Give your love,   get heart-break in ex-change,   Aft - er

all,   PEO - PLE CHANGE.   You

know as well as I,   With just the same old sky,

A bird gets might-y rest - less and has to — fly.

To Die in Summertime

17

si-lence, with-out a sin-gle sound, To touch the earth as gen-tly as a dead leaf, when it

hits the ground. To leave be-hind a mem-'ry soft as sum-mer-time, For those one

loves and has to leave be - hind. _____ To

fold as soft-ly as the grass blades fold, When wild things tram-ple them on morn-ings damp and

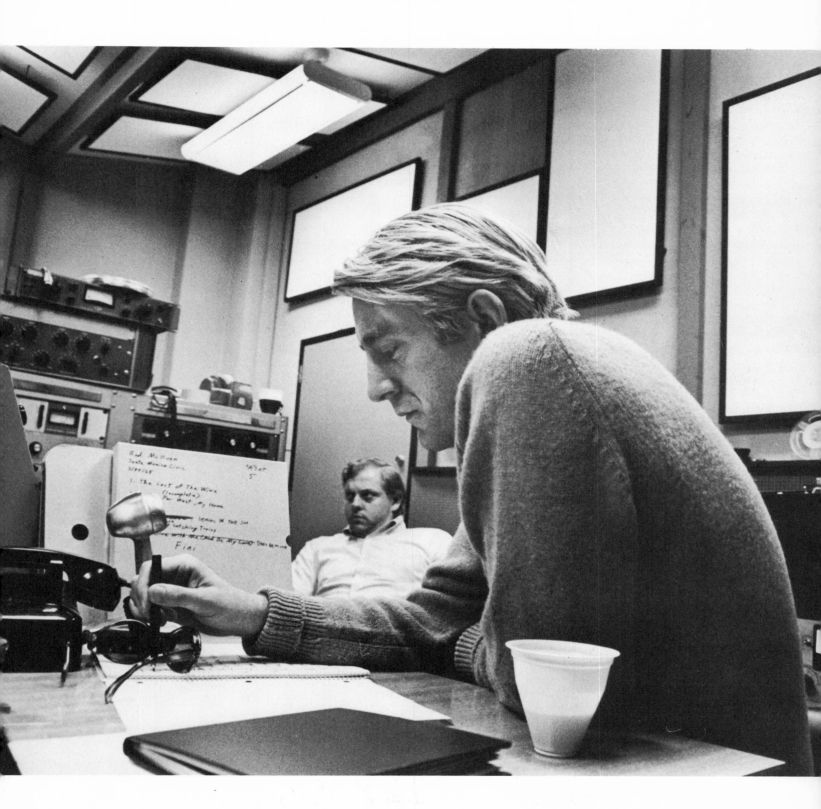

Where Are We Now?

for Charlotte Brennan

23

LOVE, LET ME NOT HUNGER

Verse:

The bum-ble bee goes from the rose to the mar-i - gold, Then goes back to the rose; The cat-er-pil-lar climbs each rib-bon of vine, 'Cause e - ven the cat-er-pil-lar knows. The day's so warm, you would-n't dare touch it, If it lay down by your side; So come to me, come to me, My arms are o - pen wide.

Slowly

Chorus:

LOVE LET ME NOT HUN-GER, —— I've been a-lone so long;

How can a lit-tle taste of wine be wrong? ———————— We'll

not get an-y young-er, Come lis-ten to my song;

And if you've had a hun-ger, Per-haps you'll sing a-long. The

Listen to the Warm

for Phillip and Jeannie Martin

33

The Beautiful Strangers

37

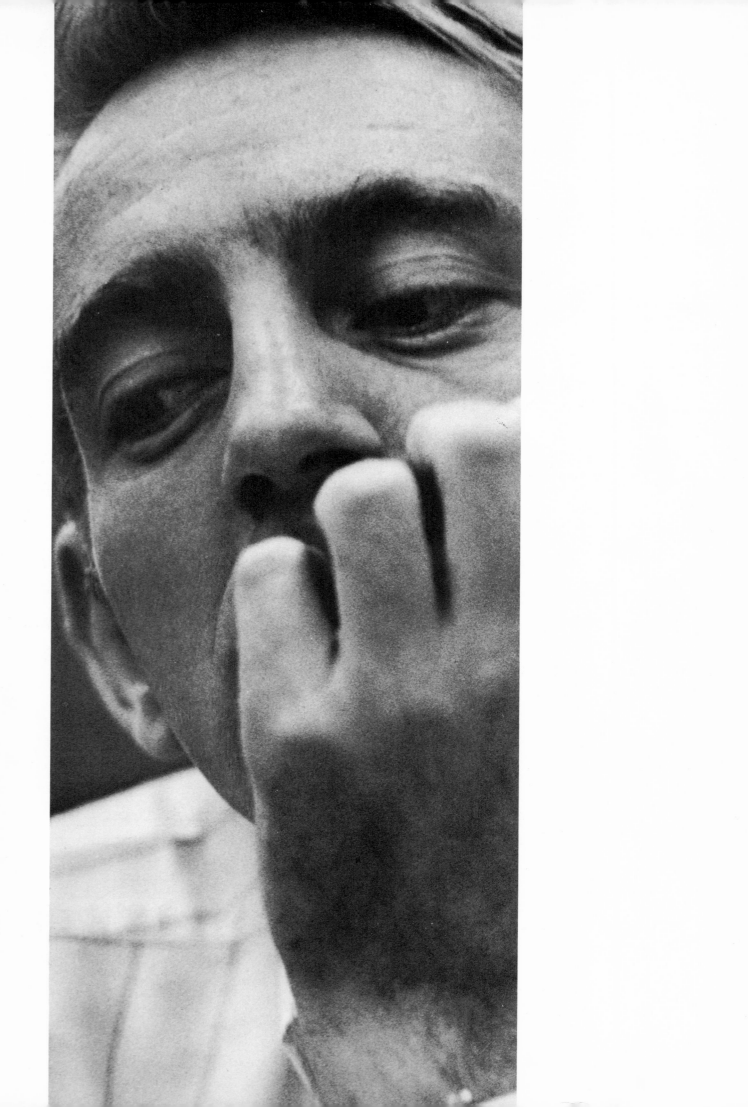

Looking Back at 30

LOOK - ING BACK AT THIR - TY, — one thing time has shown, That's
LOOK - ING BACK AT THIR - TY, it's lat - er than I thought, It's
LOOK - ING BACK AT THIR - TY, and old - er by a mile, There've
LOOK - ING BACK AT THIR - TY, — hold - ing back the tears, I

lit - tle con - so - la - tion, When you spend the day a - lone. But
bad to brood the years a - way for what I have - n't got. For
been too man - y stran - gers, that knew my crook - ed smile. And
might as well be one, — two, — three times thir - ty years. But

ev - 'ry day's an - oth - er chance, You've got to dance it like it was the fi - nal

dance; And yet a dance is just a dance and noth - ing more, You can't ex-

pect to turn each turn and find the se - cret door. _____ 2. I

2. all you touch you can - not keep, And what is love but just an-

oth er kind of sleep; And yet to sleep a - gain would be worth all the trou - bles that I've

known, Some - time I think I'm nev - er ev - er go - ing home. _____ 3. If I

oh, the crowds can be so wild, They push and tram-ple you like

some for-got-ten child; And yet I guess I've nev-er been a child at all,

Ex-cept some-times in terms of feel-ing small. _____ 4. Some

ev - 'ry day's an oth - er dance, You got-ta

dance it like it was the fi - nal dance; And if a

dance is just a dance and noth - ing more, You've got to

keep on try - ing hard to find that se - cret door. LOOK-ING BACK AT THIR - TY

That's what liv - ing's for. _____

Love Child

for Robert Fryer

Only Love

Moderato

for Sal and Jo Bonafede

1. We have ON - LY LOVE to of - fer as a prayer,
2. We have ON - LY LOVE to help us find our way,
3. We have ON - LY LOVE to keep us free from harm,

— For all the wrongs — in the world; —
— As we go out in - to the world; —
As we go a - lone in - to the world; — So

So like sing - ing — trou - ba - dours we'll go. —
So like laugh - ing chil - dren — we'll go. —
on - ly as lov - ers — we'll go. —

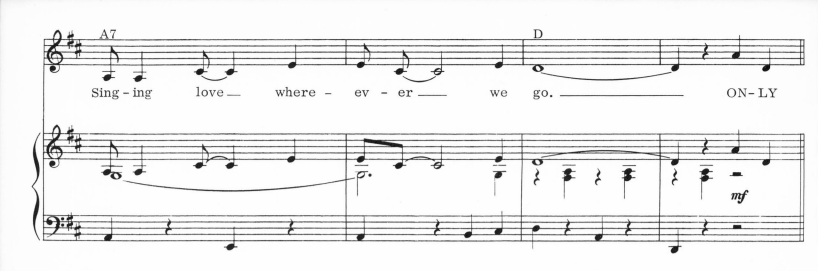

I'll Never Be Alone

63

we'll go gen-tle — in the wood; And what we do for one an-oth-er, —

will be warm and good. I'll wear your love, as one might wear a crown of lau-rel

in his hair. And then if you'll be there, I'LL NEV-ER BE — A-

LONE, I'll nev-er, ev-er be a - lone. —

When Flora Was Mine

for Neely Plumb

There was sum-mer, there was clo-ver, There was wild ___ moun-tain
There were wild deer at the cross-ing, Some-times six ___ at a

thyme; There were kids sail-in' kites on the hill-side,
time; There were white puss-y - wil-lows by the riv-er,

1. When Flo-ra Was Mine.
2. When Flo-ra Was Mine.

And Flo-ra'd run out a-long the mead-ow, Her hair fly-in' this a-way ___ and

that a - way — in the wind; Then home with her arms full of blos - soms and branch - es,

To wait for the night to be - gin. Now it's win - ter,

We've grown old - er; Me and the dan - de - li - on wine;

I'm just a fa - ther re - mem - ber - ing the time, When Flo - ra Was Mine.

Ain't You Glad You're Livin', Joe

Chasing the Sun

77

Gee, It's Nice to Be Alone

for Frank Sinatra

GEE IT'S NICE TO BE A-LONE, To wake up by your-self; To
GEE IT'S NICE TO BE A-LONE, To get to know your-self; To

own the day a-while, And not have to talk to an-y-bod-y.
waste a-way the time, And

not have to smile for an-y-bod-y. What a deal to stay in your pa-

ja-mas,— With noth-in' ver-y much to do, But watch the shad-ows

I Turn to You

The Loner

With drive

1. I have rid - den rods and bump - ers, Hitched from New York to L. A., Up from Hous - ton in Oc - to - ber, De - cem - ber down in San - ta Fe. I have walked a hun - dred high - ways

2. Been as hun - gry as the wind is, Been as thirst - y as the dust; One good rain in Am - a - ril - lo, Al - most turned my bones to rust. I have known both light and dark - ness,

3. I have heard the mad mob rag - ing, Lis - tened as they told their lies; Seen a doz - en lone - some cit - ies, Where the sun blacked out the skies. Twen - ty years I've been a Lon - er,

Cried to see the things men do; If you won-der who I am, I'm
Seen some things men should-n't see; Some-times when I held my hand out,
Not much mon - ey in my jeans; A sol - i - tar - y on - my-own-er

tacet.

Bm

A   Bm

Just a Lon - er   pass - ing   through. _____
Peo - ple turned their backs on   me. _____
Guess I know what lone - some   means. _____

Chorus   G

Bm

You know me, mis - ter, the man with the old suit-

G

case;   You know me, sis - ter, I've

Bm

F#7   3   Bm   A Bm D.C.

been ev - 'ry - where, Ain't   go - in' no - place. _____

D.C.

Fine

Methinks Thou Doth Protest Too Much

1. Look at them lit - tle girls in the min - i skirts, _____
2. Look at them hoods _____ on mo - tor - cy - cle bikes, _____
3. Look at them lil - y whites go - in' off to church, _____
4. Look at them pac - i - fists march - in' in the street, Ain't

Strut - tin' a - round and act - in' like flirts. Show - in' their thigh, _____
Roar - in' thru the neigh - bor - hood, scar - in' lit - tle tykes. Hell's Lit - tle An - gels _____
Lat - er in the aft - er - noon call - in' John Birch. Sound - in' off _____ let - ters to the
noth - in' much _____ worse than two _____ left _____ feet. Look at them _____ lit - tle kids _____

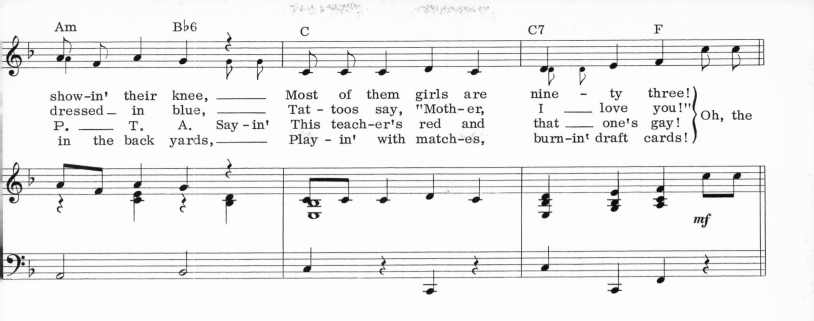

show-in' their knee, _____ Most of them girls are nine - ty three!
dressed_ in blue, _____ Tat - toos say, "Moth- er, I _____ love you!"
P. _____ T. A. Say-in' This teach-er's red and that _____ one's gay!
in the back yards,_____ Play - in' with match-es, burn-in' draft cards!
Oh, the

times, the trou - bles and tri - als are such, ME -

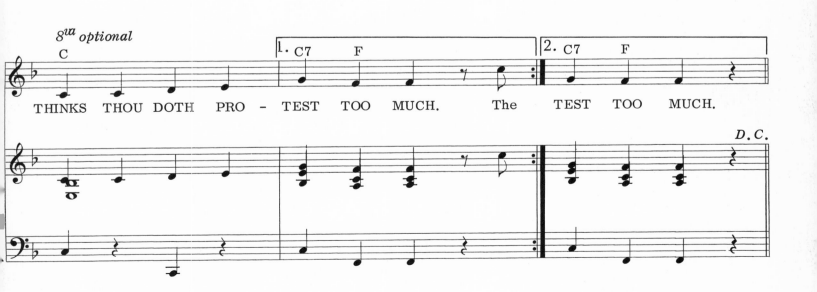

THINKS THOU DOTH PRO - TEST TOO MUCH. The TEST TOO MUCH.

8va optional

D.C.

Second Best

Something Beyond

for Liza Wilke

99

The Way It Was Before

for Flo Bennett

Slowly, with feeling

The flow-ers on the hill-side, The kites a-bove the town, The
(The) dap-pled days of danc-ing, The nights too warm to dream, When

skat-ing on the mill-pond, While the snow was fall-ing down; Ah, the years of laugh-ter, but
all the friend-ly an-i-mals would gath-er at the stream; Ah, the end-less sum-mer, but

laugh-ter comes no more,
sum-mer comes no more, } And I wish it was THE WAY IT WAS BE-FORE. The

FORE. The way it was when we could talk to one an-oth-er, With words; on-ly

The Hunters

for Lee Mendelson

THE HUNT-ERS come, THE HUNT-ERS go down dark streets danc - ing to the on - ly tunes they know; _____ And like the does in morn - ing that feed a - long the lake, Hearts are on - ly un - der - brush be-neath their feet that break. Don't wor-ry the

wind, _____ did-n't you know, _____ When the morn-ing

comes, they'll go. _____ THE HUNT-ERS

smile va-cant smiles, And the

prom-is-es they make are on-ly good a lit-tle while; For the

hunt - er   and the hunt - ed   are real - ly   quite the same,   And the

hunt-ing,   not   the lov - ing,   is the pleas-ure of   the game. Don't wor-ry   the

wind, _____   did'-nt you know, _____   When   the morn-ing

comes,   they'll go. _____

1. Fly,   bird, they're com-ing   and they'll
2. Run,   lone -some   li - on,   don't be

shoul-der / they sight ___ an-oth-er ___ doe, / They ___ quick-ly ___ make their
pleas-ure, / for the pleas-ure's ___ in ___ the pain, / And you should-n't be out ___

kill, ___ as / they ___ turn their backs / to go. } Don't wor-ry the wind, ___
walk - ing, ___ for the hunt - er comes a - gain. }

___ did-n't you know, ___ When the morn - ing

comes, they'll go. ___

About the Author

Rod McKuen was born in Oakland, California, at the end of the Depression. He grew up in California, Nevada, Washington, and Oregon, and worked as a laborer, stunt man, radio disk jockey, and newspaper columnist before serving in the Army in Japan and Korea as a psychological-warfare scriptwriter; he was a member of the Korean Civil Assistance Command.

After he returned home Mr. McKuen was encouraged by his friend Phyllis Diller to perform at San Francisco's Purple Onion. During the engagement he was brought to Hollywood and put under contract to Universal-International as an actor. In 1959 he moved to New York to compose and conduct the music for Albert McCleery's highly lauded television series *The CBS Workshop*.

Mr. McKuen has played the major cabarets and concert halls of the world, and has written more than seven hundred songs. His material has been performed by the leading entertainers and recording artists the world over. Mr. McKuen spends seven months of the year, in a house in the Hollywood hills, with a menagerie of cats and dogs, where he does most of his writing. The balance of his time he devotes to traveling and performing in Europe.

With the publication of *Stanyan Street and Other Sorrows* in 1966 and *Listen to the Warm* a year later, Mr. McKuen became the best-selling poet in America. He is currently writing screenplays for both books, and his third volume of poetry, *Lonesome Cities,* has just been published.